KS1 SATs
Arithmetic
10-Minute Tests

Hilary Koll and Steve Mills

Schofield & Sims

Introduction

This book contains 22 bite-sized tests to give you practice in answering arithmetic questions quickly.

Each test contains 12 questions and is designed to be completed in 10 minutes.

The questions are just like the questions you will need to answer in the SATs Arithmetic paper in Year 2.

What you will need

- a pencil
- an eraser
- a clock, watch or stopwatch
- an adult to time you and to mark the tests for you

How to use the book

Make sure that you are sitting in a quiet place where there aren't any distractions.

Turn to **Test 1** on page 4.

Start by answering the two warm-up questions. These will help to get you ready for the test.

Tell the adult when you have finished. They will start the timer.

Read each question carefully and write the answer. You should not use a calculator.

Work through the questions in order. Try to answer every question. If you get stuck on a question, leave it and move on to the next one. Work quickly and try to do your best.

When you reach the end of the test, stop and tell the adult that you have finished.

The adult will mark your test. Then the adult will fill in the **Total marks** and **Time taken** sections at the end of the test.

Turn to the **Progress chart** on page 48. Write your score in the box and colour the chart to show this score.

If you got some of the questions wrong, have another go at them before you look at the answers. Then ask the adult to check your work and help if you are still not sure.

Published by **Schofield & Sims Ltd**, 7 Mariner Court, Wakefield, West Yorkshire WF4 3FL, UK
Telephone 01484 607080
www.schofieldandsims.co.uk

This edition copyright © Schofield & Sims Ltd, 2019
First published in 2019
Second impression 2020

Authors: **Hilary Koll and Steve Mills**
Hilary Koll and Steve Mills have asserted their moral rights under the Copyright, Designs and Patents Act, 1988, to be identified as the authors of this work.

British Library Cataloguing in Publication Data
A catalogue record for this book is available from the British Library.

Design by **Ledgard Jepson**
Printed in the UK by **Page Bros (Norwich) Ltd**

ISBN 978 07217 1492 9

Contents

Notes for parents, teachers and other adult helpers

A pull-out answers section (pages A1 to A8) appears in the centre of this book, between pages 24 and 25. This provides answers to all the questions, along with guidance on marking the papers. Remove the pull-out section before the child begins working through the tests.

Test 1

Warm-up question	Warm-up question
3 + 4 =	6 – 5 =

1   5 + 3 =

1 mark

2   8 – 4 =

1 mark

3   99 + 1 =

1 mark

4   56 – 1 =

1 mark

5   24 + 5 =

1 mark

6   4 +  + 2 = 9

1 mark

7   64 – 20 =

1 mark

8   83 + 13 =

1 mark

9    $\frac{1}{2}$ of 6 =

1 mark

10   78 – 49 =

1 mark

11   8 ÷ 2 =

1 mark

12   73 – 10 – 10 =

1 mark

Total marks ....   Time taken ....

Test **2**

Warm-up question

2 + 6 =

Warm-up question

8 – 5 =

1 7 – [   ] = 3

1 mark

2 10 + 3 =

1 mark

3 95 + 5 =

1 mark

4 40 – 1 – 1 =

1 mark

5 21 + 30 =

1 mark

6 64 – 11 =

1 mark

7 57 + 23 =

1 mark

8 9 × 2 =

1 mark

9 $\frac{1}{2}$ of 10 =

1 mark

10 64 − 37 =

1 mark

11 10 ÷ 5 =

1 mark

12 20 + ☐ + 20 = 90

1 mark

Total marks _____   Time taken _____

Test 3

Warm-up question	Warm-up question
3 + 5 =	9 – 3 =

1   4 + 3 + 2 =

1 mark

2   11 – [＿＿＿] = 9

1 mark

3   99 + 5 =

1 mark

4   76 – 10 =

1 mark

5   5 + 31 =

1 mark

6   14 + 3 + 5 =

1 mark

7   82 – 60 =

1 mark

8   4 × 5 =

1 mark

9 $\frac{1}{2}$ of 12 =

1 mark

10   59 + 11 =

1 mark

11   80 ÷ 10 =

1 mark

12   100 – ☐ – 10 = 30

1 mark

Total marks ....   Time taken ....

Test 4

Warm-up question

Warm-up question

$7 + 2 =$

Warm-up question

$14 - 4 =$

1 $\boxed{} = 5 + 6$

2 $16 - 12 =$

1 mark

3 $99 + 8 =$

1 mark

4 $\boxed{} = 20 - 1$

1 mark

5 $27 + 5 + 2 =$

1 mark

6 $86 - 50 =$

1 mark

7 54 + 33 =

1 mark

8 5 × 10 =

1 mark

9 $\frac{1}{2}$ of 20 =

1 mark

10 76 − 69 =

1 mark

11 14 ÷ 2 =

1 mark

12 70 − 5 − 5 =

1 mark

Total marks .... Time taken ....

Test **5**

Warm-up question 6 + 4 =	Warm-up question $\boxed{}$ = 9 – 7

1 17 + 5 =	2 16 – 6 =
3 98 + 11 =	4 $\boxed{}$ = 25 – 2
5 53 + 31 =	6 87 – 27 =

1 mark

7   16 + 46 =

1 mark

8 $\frac{1}{2}$ of 14 =

1 mark

9   2 ÷ 2 =

1 mark

10   + 40 = 70

1 mark

11   6 × 5 =

1 mark

12   6 + 2 + 7 =

1 mark

Total marks ....   Time taken ....

Test **6**

Warm-up question

Warm-up question

10 + 5 =

Warm-up question

8 − 6 =

1   9 + 2 + 7 =

1 mark

2   [   ] = 5 + 4 + 1

1 mark

3   99 + 14 =

1 mark

4   68 − 5 =

1 mark

5   36 + 54 =

1 mark

6   77 − 43 =

1 mark

7   45 + 27 =

1 mark

8   10 × 10 =

1 mark

9 $\frac{1}{2}$ of 18 =

1 mark

10   [ ] − 51 = 19

1 mark

11   100 ÷ 10 =

1 mark

12   99 − [ ] = 49

1 mark

Total marks ....   Time taken ....

Test 7

Warm-up question	Warm-up question
8 + 0 =	17 − 7 =

1 4 + 7 + 5 =

1 mark

2 10 −  = 1

1 mark

3 4 × 2 =

1 mark

4 $\frac{1}{2}$ of 2 =

1 mark

5 18 + 57 =

1 mark

6 8 + 5 + 3 =

1 mark

7   70 − 30 =

1 mark

8   73 − 40 =

1 mark

9   8 × 5 =

1 mark

10   78 − [   ] = 71

1 mark

11   45 ÷ 5 =

1 mark

12   77 − 10 − 10 =

1 mark

Total marks ....   Time taken ....

Test 8

1 $14 + 3 + 2 =$

1 mark

2 $20 - \boxed{} = 15$

1 mark

3 $3 \times 10 =$

1 mark

4 $37 + 23 =$

1 mark

5 $93 - 19 =$

1 mark

6 $34 + 58 =$

1 mark

7 20 + 50 + 30 =

1 mark

8 1 × 2 =

1 mark

9  $\frac{1}{2}$ of 22 =

1 mark

10 ☐ + 47 = 80

1 mark

11 10 ÷ 10 =

1 mark

12 92 − 60 =

1 mark

Total marks ....   Time taken ....

Test 9

Warm-up question

$15 = 17 -$ [   ]

Warm-up question

$89 + 1 =$

[   ]

1 $8 + 9 + 6 =$

[   ] [ ]
1 mark

2 [   ] $+ 1 + 1 = 8$

[ ]
1 mark

3 $3 \times 5 =$

[   ] [ ]
1 mark

4 $77 - 9 =$

[   ] [ ]
1 mark

5 $47 + 50 =$

[   ] [ ]
1 mark

6 $82 - 46 =$

[   ] [ ]
1 mark

7   70 −  = 60

1 mark

8   7 × 5 =

1 mark

9 $\frac{1}{4}$ of 4 =

1 mark

10   48 − 2 − 2 =

1 mark

11   12 ÷ 2 =

1 mark

12    × 2 = 10

1 mark

Total marks ....   Time taken ....

Test 10

1   ☐ = 40 − 4

1 mark

2   22 + 6 + 6 =

1 mark

3   7 × 10 =

1 mark

4   72 − 40 =

1 mark

5   5 + 8 + 4 =

1 mark

6   38 + 55 =

1 mark

7 [___] + 40 = 80

1 mark

8 50 ÷ 5 =

1 mark

9 65 + 5 + 5 + 5 =

1 mark

10 $\frac{1}{4}$ of 12 =

1 mark

11 5 × 5 =

1 mark

12 81 − 36 =

1 mark

Total marks ....   Time taken ....

Test 11

Warm-up question

7 + 6 =

Warm-up question

60 − [ ] = 59

1 10 − [ ] − 1 = 6

1 mark

2 5 + 71 =

1 mark

3 8 × 2 =

1 mark

4 75 − 42 =

1 mark

5 16 + 74 =

1 mark

6 59 − 14 =

1 mark

KS1 SATs Arithmetic 10-Minute Tests

Notes for parents, teachers and other adult helpers

KS1 SATs Arithmetic 10-Minute Tests are short, timed tests designed to build speed and fluency.

The questions in the tests closely match the questions children will need to answer in the Key Stage 1 SATs Arithmetic paper, which is taken in Year 2. As children work through the book, the tests get progressively more challenging.

It is intended that children will take around 10 minutes to complete each test. However, SATs papers are not strictly timed at this age, so allow them longer if they need it.

How to use the book

Remove this pull-out section before giving the book to the child.

Before the child begins work on the first test, together read the instructions on page 2. As you do so, point out to the child that there is a target time of 10 minutes for completing the test.

Make sure the child has all the equipment in the list headed **What will you need** on page 2.

Be sure that the child knows to tell you clearly when they have finished the test.

When the child is ready, say 'Start the test now' and make a note of the start time.

When the child has finished, make a note of the end time and then work out how long they took to complete the test. Then fill in the **Time taken** section, which appears at the end of the test.

Mark the child's answers using this pull-out section. Each test is out of 12 marks and each individual question is worth one mark. Then complete the **Total marks** section at the end of the test.

Turn to the **Progress chart** on page 48. Encourage the child to write their score in the box and colour the chart to show this score.

Whatever the test score, always encourage the child to have another go at the questions that they got wrong – without looking at the answers. If the child's answers are still incorrect, work through these questions together. Demonstrate the correct method if necessary.

If the child struggles with particular question types (for example, questions involving fractions), help them to develop the skills and strategies needed.

Ask them to complete the next test at a later date, once they have had sufficient time to practise any question types they found difficult.

Answers

Test 1 (page 4)

Warm-up question 3 + 4 = 7	Warm-up question 6 − 5 = 1
1 5 + 3 = 8	**2** 8 − 4 = 4
3 99 + 1 = 100	**4** 56 − 1 = 55
5 24 + 5 = 29	**6** 4 + 3 + 2 = 9
7 64 − 20 = 44	**8** 83 + 13 = 96
9 $\frac{1}{2}$ of 6 = 3	**10** 78 − 49 = 29
11 8 ÷ 2 = 4	**12** 73 − 10 − 10 = 53

Test 2 (page 6)

Warm-up question 2 + 6 = 8	Warm-up question 8 − 5 = 3
1 7 − 4 = 3	**2** 10 + 3 = 13
3 95 + 5 = 100	**4** 40 − 1 − 1 = 38
5 21 + 30 = 51	**6** 64 − 11 = 53
7 57 + 23 = 80	**8** 9 × 2 = 18
9 $\frac{1}{2}$ of 10 = 5	**10** 64 − 37 = 27
11 10 ÷ 5 = 2	**12** 20 + 50 + 20 = 90

Test 3 (page 8)

Warm-up question 3 + 5 = 8	Warm-up question 9 − 3 = 6
1 4 + 3 + 2 = 9	**2** 11 − 2 = 9
3 99 + 5 = 104	**4** 76 − 10 = 66
5 5 + 31 = 36	**6** 14 + 3 + 5 = 22
7 82 − 60 = 22	**8** 4 × 5 = 20
9 $\frac{1}{2}$ of 12 = 6	**10** 59 + 11 = 70
11 80 ÷ 10 = 8	**12** 100 − 60 − 10 = 30

Test 4 (page 10)

Warm-up question 7 + 2 = 9	Warm-up question 14 − 4 = 10
1 11 = 5 + 6	**2** 16 − 12 = 4
3 99 + 8 = 107	**4** 19 = 20 − 1
5 27 + 5 + 2 = 34	**6** 86 − 50 = 36
7 54 + 33 = 87	**8** 5 × 10 = 50
9 $\frac{1}{2}$ of 20 = 10	**10** 76 − 69 = 7
11 14 ÷ 2 = 7	**12** 70 − 5 − 5 = 60

Test 5 (page 12)

Warm-up question 6 + 4 = 10	Warm-up question 2 = 9 – 7
1 17 + 5 = 22	2 16 – 6 = 10
3 98 + 11 = 109	4 23 = 25 – 2
5 53 + 31 = 84	6 87 – 27 = 60
7 16 + 46 = 62	8 $\frac{1}{2}$ of 14 = 7
9 2 ÷ 2 = 1	10 30 + 40 = 70
11 6 × 5 = 30	12 6 + 2 + 7 = 15

Test 6 (page 14)

Warm-up question 10 + 5 = 15	Warm-up question 8 – 6 = 2
1 9 + 2 + 7 = 18	2 10 = 5 + 4 + 1
3 99 + 14 = 113	4 68 – 5 = 63
5 36 + 54 = 90	6 77 – 43 = 34
7 45 + 27 = 72	8 10 × 10 = 100
9 $\frac{1}{2}$ of 18 = 9	10 70 – 51 = 19
11 100 ÷ 10 = 10	12 99 – 50 = 49

Test 7 (page 16)

Warm-up question 8 + 0 = 8	Warm-up question 17 – 7 = 10
1 4 + 7 + 5 = 16	2 10 – 9 = 1
3 4 × 2 = 8	4 $\frac{1}{2}$ of 2 = 1
5 18 + 57 = 75	6 8 + 5 + 3 = 16
7 70 – 30 = 40	8 73 – 40 = 33
9 8 × 5 = 40	10 78 – 7 = 71
11 45 ÷ 5 = 9	12 77 – 10 – 10 = 57

Test 8 (page 18)

Warm-up question 8 + 8 = 16	Warm-up question 48 + 1 + 1 = 50
1 14 + 3 + 2 = 19	2 20 – 5 = 15
3 3 × 10 = 30	4 37 + 23 = 60
5 93 – 19 = 74	6 34 + 58 = 92
7 20 + 50 + 30 = 100	8 1 × 2 = 2
9 $\frac{1}{2}$ of 22 = 11	10 33 + 47 = 80
11 10 ÷ 10 = 1	12 92 – 60 = 32

Answers

Test 9 (page 20)

Warm-up question $15 = 17 - 2$	Warm-up question $89 + 1 = 90$
1 $8 + 9 + 6 = 23$	**2** $6 + 1 + 1 = 8$
3 $3 \times 5 = 15$	**4** $77 - 9 = 68$
5 $47 + 50 = 97$	**6** $82 - 46 = 36$
7 $70 - 10 = 60$	**8** $7 \times 5 = 35$
9 $\frac{1}{4}$ of $4 = 1$	**10** $48 - 2 - 2 = 44$
11 $12 \div 2 = 6$	**12** $5 \times 2 = 10$

Test 10 (page 22)

Warm-up question $13 + 5 = 18$	Warm-up question $70 - 1 - 1 = 68$
1 $36 = 40 - 4$	**2** $22 + 6 + 6 = 34$
3 $7 \times 10 = 70$	**4** $72 - 40 = 32$
5 $5 + 8 + 4 = 17$	**6** $38 + 55 = 93$
7 $40 + 40 = 80$	**8** $50 \div 5 = 10$
9 $65 + 5 + 5 + 5 = 80$	**10** $\frac{1}{4}$ of $12 = 3$
11 $5 \times 5 = 25$	**12** $81 - 36 = 45$

Test 11 (page 24)

Warm-up question $7 + 6 = 13$	Warm-up question $60 - 1 = 59$
1 $10 - 3 - 1 = 6$	**2** $5 + 71 = 76$
3 $8 \times 2 = 16$	**4** $75 - 42 = 33$
5 $16 + 74 = 90$	**6** $59 - 14 = 45$
7 $\frac{1}{2}$ of $16 = 8$	**8** $70 \div 10 = 7$
9 $10 + 40 + 30 = 80$	**10** $94 - 10 - 10 = 74$
11 $3 \div 3 = 1$	**12** $55 - 8 = 47$

Test 12 (page 26)

Warm-up question $8 + 3 + 2 = 13$	Warm-up question $67 - 1 = 66$
1 $11 = 16 - 5$	**2** $77 - 13 = 64$
3 $6 \times 2 = 12$	**4** $23 + 49 = 72$
5 $97 - 57 = 40$	**6** $83 - 48 = 35$
7 $100 - 80 = 20$	**8** $2 \times 9 = 18$
9 $\frac{1}{4}$ of $16 = 4$	**10** $78 + 2 + 2 + 2 = 84$
11 $35 \div 5 = 7$	**12** $58 - 12 = 46$

Test 13 (page 28)

Warm-up question 12 − 5 = 7	Warm-up question 99 + 2 + 1 = 102
1 10 + 11 = 21	**2** 32 + 50 = 82
3 80 + 20 = 100	**4** 67 − 37 = 30
5 46 + 19 = 65	**6** 82 − 58 = 24
7 7 × 2 = 14	**8** 40 ÷ 5 = 8
9 $\frac{1}{4}$ of 20 = 5	**10** 85 − 5 − 5 = 75
11 50 ÷ 10 = 5	**12** 43 + 35 = 78

Test 14 (page 30)

Warm-up question 9 + 6 = 15	Warm-up question 80 − 1 − 2 = 77
1 12 = 15 − 3	**2** 6 + 2 + 9 = 17
3 40 + 50 = 90	**4** 87 + 5 + 4 = 96
5 59 − 17 = 42	**6** 16 + 58 = 74
7 9 × 5 = 45	**8** 16 ÷ 2 = 8
9 43 + 10 + 10 + 10 = 73	**10** $\frac{1}{4}$ of 40 = 10
11 6 × 2 = 12	**12** 84 − 39 = 45

Test 15 (page 32)

Warm-up question 18 − 6 = 12	Warm-up question $\frac{1}{2}$ of 4 = 2
1 8 + 4 = 12	**2** 47 − 13 = 34
3 30 + 20 + 30 = 80	**4** 58 + 27 = 85
5 97 − 64 = 33	**6** 56 − 48 = 8
7 12 × 5 = 60	**8** 11 × 10 = 110
9 70 − 2 − 2 − 2 = 64	**10** $\frac{1}{4}$ of 24 = 6
11 24 ÷ 2 = 12	**12** 88 − 79 = 9

Test 16 (page 34)

Warm-up question 12 + 7 = 19	Warm-up question 100 − 5 = 95
1 10 − 9 = 1	**2** 32 + 7 = 39
3 70 − 50 = 20	**4** 57 − 14 = 43
5 86 − 31 = 55	**6** 91 − 48 = 43
7 12 × 10 = 120	**8** 18 ÷ 2 = 9
9 $\frac{1}{3}$ of 30 = 10	**10** 101 − 10 − 10 = 81
11 45 ÷ 5 = 9	**12** 47 + 18 = 65

Answers

Test **17** (page 36)

Warm-up question $17 - 3 = 14$	Warm-up question $\frac{1}{2}$ of 8 = 4
1 $7 + 5 + 2 = 14$	**2** $63 + 12 = 75$
3 $100 - 70 = 30$	**4** $74 + 19 = 93$
5 $97 - 44 = 53$	**6** $82 - 38 = 44$
7 $5 \div 5 = 1$	**8** $30 - 3 - 3 = 24$
9 $53 + 30 + 5 = 88$	**10** $37 + 40 = 77$
11 $11 \times 5 = 55$	**12** $\frac{3}{4}$ of 4 = 3

Test **18** (page 38)

Warm-up question $9 + 7 = 16$	Warm-up question $101 - 5 = 96$
1 $16 + 15 = 31$	**2** $64 - 50 = 14$
3 $30 + 20 + 30 = 80$	**4** $53 + 37 = 90$
5 $78 - 35 = 43$	**6** $93 - 86 = 7$
7 $15 \div 5 = 3$	**8** $18 + 3 + 3 + 3 = 27$
9 $\frac{3}{4}$ of 40 = 30	**10** $12 \times 2 = 24$
11 $69 - 7 = 62$	**12** $94 - 10 - 10 - 10 = 64$

Test **19** (page 40)

Warm-up question $19 + 3 + 3 = 25$	Warm-up question $97 + 3 = 100$
1 $27 - 3 - 3 - 3 = 18$	**2** $83 - 7 = 76$
3 $50 = 90 - 40$	**4** $48 + 37 = 85$
5 $98 - 70 = 28$	**6** $91 - 49 = 42$
7 $\frac{3}{4}$ of 80 = 60	**8** $5 \times 0 = 0$
9 $\frac{2}{4}$ of 50 = 25	**10** $17 + 80 = 97$
11 $5 \div 1 = 5$	**12** $\frac{3}{4}$ of 8 = 6

Test **20** (page 42)

Warm-up question $14 - 5 = 9$	Warm-up question $\frac{1}{2}$ of 40 = 20
1 $18 - 2 = 16$	**2** $73 - 50 = 23$
3 $100 - 30 = 70$	**4** $75 - 38 = 37$
5 $29 + 16 = 45$	**6** $26 + 58 = 84$
7 $22 \div 2 = 11$	**8** $13 + 15 + 3 = 31$
9 $\frac{1}{4}$ of 100 = 25	**10** $\frac{2}{4}$ of 40 = 20
11 $5 \times 12 = 60$	**12** $11 \times 3 = 33$

Test 21 (page 44)

Warm-up question	Warm-up question
$11 + 8 + 2 = 21$	$100 - 30 = 70$
1 $\frac{1}{3}$ of $12 = 4$	2 $76 + 24 = 100$
3 $90 - 40 = 50$	4 $63 - 49 = 14$
5 $92 - 14 = 78$	6 $12 + 3 + 3 + 3 = 21$
7 $60 \div 5 = 12$	8 $7 \times 3 = 21$
9 $\frac{2}{4}$ of $20 = 10$	10 $99 - 70 = 29$
11 $120 \div 10 = 12$	12 $30 + 60 + 20 = 110$

Test 22 (page 46)

Warm-up question	Warm-up question
$\frac{1}{3}$ of $9 = 3$	$101 - 12 = 89$
1 $13 = 18 - 5$	2 $35 + 59 = 94$
3 $30 + 30 + 0 = 60$	4 $71 - 48 = 23$
5 $17 + 48 = 65$	6 $24 - 3 - 3 - 3 = 15$
7 $55 \div 5 = 11$	8 $9 \times 3 = 27$
9 $\frac{3}{4}$ of $12 = 9$	10 $50 + 26 = 76$
11 $0 \times 10 = 0$	12 $\frac{1}{3}$ of $60 = 20$

This book of answers is a pull-out section from **KS1 SATs Arithmetic 10-Minute Tests**.

Published by **Schofield & Sims Ltd**, 7 Mariner Court, Wakefield, West Yorkshire WF4 3FL, UK
Telephone 01484 607080
www.schofieldandsims.co.uk

Authors: **Hilary Koll and Steve Mills**
Hilary Koll and Steve Mills have asserted their moral rights under the Copyright, Designs and Patents Act, 1988, to be identified as the authors of this work.

British Library Cataloguing in Publication Data
A catalogue record for this book is available from the British Library.

Design by **Ledgard Jepson**
Printed in the UK by **Page Bros (Norwich) Ltd**

ISBN 978 07217 1492 9

7 $\frac{1}{2}$ of 16 =

1 mark

8 70 ÷ 10 =

1 mark

9 10 + 40 + 30 =

1 mark

10 94 − 10 − 10 =

1 mark

11 3 ÷ 3 =

1 mark

12 55 − ⬚ = 47

1 mark

Total marks .... Time taken ....

Test 12

Warm-up question

$8 + 3 + 2 =$

Warm-up question

$67 - 1 =$

1 $\boxed{} = 16 - 5$

1 mark

2 $77 - 13 =$

1 mark

3 $6 \times 2 =$

1 mark

4 $23 + 49 =$

1 mark

5 $97 - 57 =$

1 mark

6 $83 - 48 =$

1 mark

7 100 − ☐ = 20

1 mark

8 2 × 9 =

1 mark

9 $\frac{1}{4}$ of 16 =

1 mark

10 78 + 2 + 2 + 2 =

1 mark

11 35 ÷ 5 =

1 mark

12 ☐ − 12 = 46

1 mark

Total marks .... Time taken ....

Test **13**

Warm-up question 12 – 5 =	Warm-up question 99 + 2 + 1 =

1 10 + [ ] = 21

1 mark

2 32 + 50 =

1 mark

3 [ ] + 20 = 100

1 mark

4 67 – 37 =

1 mark

5 46 + 19 =

1 mark

6 82 – 58 =

1 mark

7 7 × 2 =

1 mark

8 40 ÷ 5 =

1 mark

9 $\frac{1}{4}$ of 20 =

1 mark

10 85 – 5 – 5 =

1 mark

11  ÷ 10 = 5

1 mark

12 43 + [ ] = 78

1 mark

Total marks ....   Time taken ....

Test 14

Warm-up question

$9 + 6 =$

Warm-up question

$80 - 1 - 2 =$

---

1 [   ] $= 15 - 3$

☐
1 mark

2 $6 + 2 + 9 =$

☐ ☐
1 mark

---

3 $40 +$ [   ] $= 90$

☐
1 mark

4 $87 + 5 + 4 =$

☐ ☐
1 mark

---

5 $59 - 17 =$

☐ ☐
1 mark

6 $16 + 58 =$

☐ ☐
1 mark

7 9 × 5 =

[___] [ ] 1 mark

8 16 ÷ 2 =

[___] [ ] 1 mark

9 43 + 10 + 10 + 10 =

[___] [ ] 1 mark

10 $\frac{1}{4}$ of 40 =

[___] [ ] 1 mark

11  × 2 = 12

[ ] 1 mark

12 84 − 39 =

[___] [ ] 1 mark

Total marks ....   Time taken ....

Test **15**

Warm-up question

18 − 6 =

Warm-up question

$\frac{1}{2}$ of 4 =

1   8 +  = 12

1 mark

2   47 − 13 =

1 mark

3   30 + 20 + 30 =

1 mark

4   58 + 27 =

1 mark

5   97 − 64 =

1 mark

6   56 − 48 =

1 mark

7 12 × 5 =

1 mark

8 11 × 10 =

1 mark

9 70 – 2 – 2 – 2 =

1 mark

10 $\frac{1}{4}$ of 24 =

1 mark

11 24 ÷ 2 =

1 mark

12 ⬜ – 79 = 9

1 mark

Total marks .... Time taken ....

Test 16

Warm-up question

12 + 7 =

Warm-up question

100 − 5 =

1   10 − [   ] = 1

1 mark

2   32 + 7 =

1 mark

3   [   ] − 50 = 20

1 mark

4   57 − 14 =

1 mark

5   86 − 31 =

1 mark

6   91 − 48 =

1 mark

7 12 × 10 =

1 mark

8 18 ÷ 2 =

1 mark

9 $\frac{1}{3}$ of 30 =

1 mark

10 101 − 10 − 10 =

1 mark

11 ☐ ÷ 5 = 9

1 mark

12 47 + ☐ = 65

1 mark

Total marks .... Time taken ....

Test **17**

Warm-up question	Warm-up question
17 − 3 =	$\frac{1}{2}$ of 8 =

1 ☐ + 5 + 2 = 14

1 mark

2 63 + 12 =

1 mark

3 100 − ☐ = 30

1 mark

4 74 + 19 =

1 mark

5 97 − 44 =

1 mark

6 82 − 38 =

1 mark

7   5 ÷ 5 =

1 mark

8   30 – 3 – 3 =

1 mark

9   53 + 30 + 5 =

1 mark

10   37+ ⬚ = 77

1 mark

11   11 × 5 =

1 mark

12 $\frac{3}{4}$ of 4 =

1 mark

Total marks ....   Time taken ....

Test 18

$9 +$ ☐ $= 16$

$101 - 5 =$

1 ☐ $+ 15 = 31$

1 mark

2 $64 - 50 =$

1 mark

3 $30 + 20 +$ $= 80$

1 mark

4 $53 + 37 =$

1 mark

5 $78 - 35 =$

1 mark

6 $93 - 86 =$

1 mark

7 $15 \div 5 =$

1 mark

8 $18 + 3 + 3 + 3 =$

1 mark

9 $\frac{3}{4}$ of 40 =

1 mark

10 $12 \times 2 =$

1 mark

11 69 – [ ] = 62

1 mark

12 $94 - 10 - 10 - 10 =$

1 mark

Total marks .... Time taken ....

Test 19

Warm-up question	Warm-up question
19 + 3 + 3 =	97 + 3 =

1 27 – 3 – 3 – 3 =

1 mark

2 83 – 7 =

1 mark

3 ⬜ = 90 – 40

1 mark

4 48 + 37 =

1 mark

5 98 – ⬜ = 28

1 mark

6 91 – 49 =

1 mark

7 $\frac{3}{4}$ of 80 =

1 mark

8 5 × 0 =

1 mark

9 $\frac{2}{4}$ of 50 =

1 mark

10 17 +  = 97

1 mark

11 5 ÷ [ ] = 5

1 mark

12 $\frac{3}{4}$ of 8 =

1 mark

Total marks ....   Time taken ....

Test **20**

1. $\boxed{} - 2 = 16$

   1 mark

2. $73 - 50 =$

   1 mark

3. $100 - \boxed{} = 70$

   1 mark

4. $75 - 38 =$

   1 mark

5. $29 + \boxed{} = 45$

   1 mark

6. $26 + 58 =$

   1 mark

7 22 ÷ 2 =

1 mark

8 13 + 15 + 3 =

1 mark

9 $\frac{1}{4}$ of 100 =

1 mark

10 $\frac{2}{4}$ of 40 =

1 mark

11 5 × 12 =

1 mark

12 11 × 3 =

1 mark

Total marks .... Time taken ....

Test **21**

Warm-up question	Warm-up question
11 + 8 + 2 =	100 – 30 =

1 $\frac{1}{3}$ of 12 =

1 mark

2 76 + 24 =

1 mark

3 [　　　] – 40 = 50

1 mark

4 63 – 49 =

1 mark

5 92 – [　　　] = 78

1 mark

6 12 + 3 + 3 + 3 =

1 mark

7   60 ÷ 5 =

1 mark

8   7 × 3 =

1 mark

9   $\frac{2}{4}$ of 20 =

1 mark

10   ⬜ − 70 = 29

1 mark

11   120 ÷ 10 =

1 mark

12   30 + 60 + 20 =

1 mark

Total marks ....   Time taken ....

Test **22**

Warm-up question

$\frac{1}{3}$ of 9 =

Warm-up question

101 − 12 =

1 13 = [ ] − 5

1 mark

2 35 + 59 =

1 mark

3 [ ] + 30 + 0 = 60

1 mark

4 71 − 48 =

1 mark

5 17 + [ ] = 65

1 mark

6 24 − 3 − 3 − 3 =

1 mark

7 $55 \div 5 =$

1 mark

8 $9 \times 3 =$

1 mark

9 $\frac{3}{4}$ of $12 =$

1 mark

10 $\boxed{} + 26 = 76$

1 mark

11 $\boxed{} \times 10 = 0$

1 mark

12 $\frac{1}{3}$ of $60 =$

1 mark

Total marks ....   Time taken ....

Progress chart

Write the score (out of 12) for each test in the box provided to the right of the chart.
Then colour the row next to the box to represent this score.

													Total
Test 1													
Test 2													
Test 3													
Test 4													
Test 5													
Test 6													
Test 7													
Test 8													
Test 9													
Test 10													
Test 11													
Test 12													
Test 13													
Test 14													
Test 15													
Test 16													
Test 17													
Test 18													
Test 19													
Test 20													
Test 21													
Test 22													
	1	2	3	4	5	6	7	8	9	10	11	12	

Score (out of 12)